W9-CPE-620

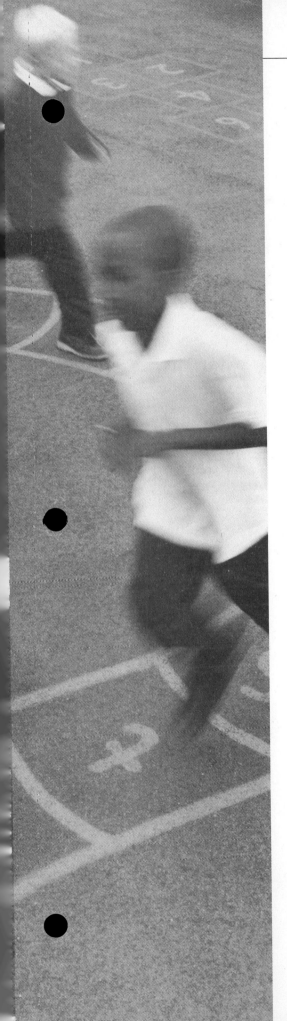

Social Studies Alive!®
My School and Family

TCi™

Chief Executive Officer
Bert Bower

Chief Operating Officer
Amy Larson

Director of Product Development
Maria Favata

Strategic Product Manager
Nathan Wellborne

Content Developer
Ginger Wu

Senior Strategic Editor
Kim Merlino

Program Editors and Writers
Mikaila Garfinkel
Alex White
Ginger Wu

Production Manager
Jodi Forrest

Operations & Software Manager
Marsha Ifurung

Designer
Sarah Osentowski

Art Direction
Julia Foug

Teachers' Curriculum Institute
PO Box 1327
Rancho Cordova, CA 95741

Customer Service: 800-497-6138
www.teachtci.com

ISBN 978-1-58371-090-6
1 2 3 4 5 6 7 8 9 10 -DB- 20 19 18 17 16 15

Manufactured by Hess Print Solutions, Brimfield, OH
United States of America, August 2015, Job 261279

Program Consultant

Vicki LaBoskey, Ph.D.
Professor of Education
Mills College, Oakland, California

Reading Specialist

Barbara Schubert, Ph.D.
Reading Specialist
Saint Mary's College, Moraga, California

Social Studies Content Scholars

Paul A. Barresi, J.D., Ph.D.
Professor of Political Science and Environmental
Law
*Southern New Hampshire University, Manchester,
New Hampshire*

Phillip J. VanFossen, Ph.D.
James F. Ackerman Professor of Social Studies
Education and Associate Director, Purdue Center
for Economic Education
Purdue University, West Lafayette, Indiana

Fred Walk
Lecturer, Department of Geography
Instructional Assistant Professor, Department of
History
Illinois State University, Normal, Illinois

Wyatt Wells, Ph.D.
Professor of History
Auburn Montgomery, Alabama

Literature Consultant

Regina M. Rees, Ph.D.
Assistant Professor
*Beeghly College of Education, Youngstown State
University, Youngstown, Ohio*

Teacher Consultants

Jill Bartky
Teacher
*Sharp Park Elementary School,
Pacifica, California*

Debra Elsen
Teacher
Manchester Elementary, Manchester, Maryland

Gina Frazzini
Literary Coach
Gatzert Elementary, Seattle, Washington

Patrick J. Lee
Teacher
Ohlone Elementary, Palo Alto, California

Jennifer Miley
Teacher
Duveneck Elementary School, Palo Alto, California

Mitch Pascal
Social Studies Specialist
Arlington County Schools, Arlington, Virginia

Jodi Perraud
Teacher
*Boulevard Heights Elementary,
Hollywood, Florida*

Becky Suthers
Retired Teacher
*Stephen F. Austin Elementary,
Weatherford, Texas*

Contents

13 Where Do Families Live?

14 What Are Family Traditions?

15 What Do Good Neighbors Do?

These two goats cannot pass on the bridge.

What will happen next? Draw your ideas.

Circle 2 ways we share.

Circle 2 ways we talk.

Circle 2 ways we listen.

Circle 2 ways we take turns.

When do you play fairly? How are you a good sport?

Use words and pictures.

Put the story in order. Use numbers 1 through 4.

 At a neighborhood meeting, both sides listen. They agree to share the lot.

 Maya's grandma sees an empty lot. She wants to plant a garden.

 People work together. They put in a garden and basketball courts.

 Maya's grandma goes to City Hall. She learns another group wants to put basketball courts on the lot.

How could you use this empty lot?

Draw what your class chooses to do.

Our _____

What else can we do to get along in school?

Draw a picture. Write a sentence.

First answer the questions for yourself.

Then shake hands with a friend.

Say hello. Ask the same questions.

		Me	Classmate
	Do you like to dance?		
	Are you a girl?		
	Do you feel happy today?		
	Are you 6 years old?		
	Are you a boy?		
	Do you like to draw?		
	Do you like sports?		
	Have you lost a tooth?		

Write a word in each blank. Draw a picture
for each pair of sentences.

Part A

Each of us is special.

_____ makes me special.

Part B

We are good at different things.

I am good at _____ .

Part C

> You can learn from me.
>
>
>
>
>
>
>
> I can help you _____.

Part D

> I can learn from you.
>
>
>
>
>
>
>
> You can help me _____.

It is summer. What is the grasshopper doing?

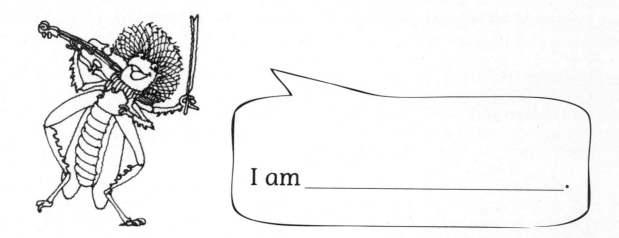

I am _____.

Now it is winter. How does the grasshopper feel?

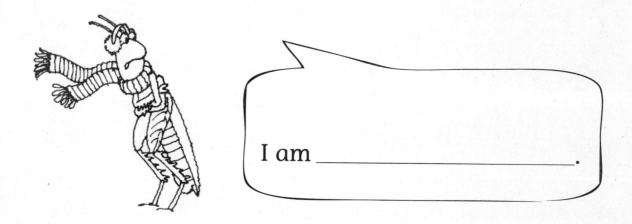

I am _____.

What lesson did the grasshopper learn from the ant?

_____

_____

● Think of a different lesson.

Let's say the ant learned from the grasshopper.

The grasshopper was good at something.

What was it? What could the ant have learned?

> I am good at _____.
>
> I can help you learn _____
>
> _____.

Write your partner's name on Handout C.

Color the gift. Follow this key.

Is your partner a boy or a girl?

Use the matching crayon.

Color the ribbon on the gift.

Girl

Boy

What does your partner like to do?

Use the key to color the rest of the gift.

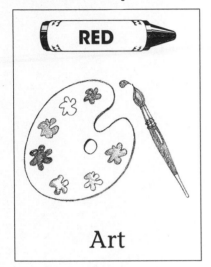

Art

Music

Talking

Athletics

Solving problems

Make-believe

Reading

What is one rule in your home?

Draw a picture.

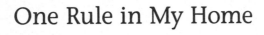

One Rule in My Home

Where are all the children getting along?

Circle the picture.

Where are the children being safe?

Circle the picture.

Where are the children being fair?

Circle the picture.

Where are the children learning?

Circle the picture.

Why do we have these rules at school?

Rules   **Reasons**

We do our best work.		Helps us get along.
We take turns.		Helps us learn.
We walk in the halls.		Helps us be safe.

Should this be a law?

How did the whole class vote?   Yes   No

How did the leaders vote?   Yes   No

Why is it good to have leaders vote for the laws?

_____

_____

_____

This law helps us be safe.

What is another law that helps us be safe on city streets?

Who could help you find another law? _____

Where could you look? _____

Draw a picture of the law. Show how it keeps us safe.

What is one class rule? Write it here:

_____

Draw what happens when you follow the rule.

Draw what might happen if you break the rule.

Who helps you at your school? Draw a picture.

Choose a word to match each picture.

Word Bank

Principal   Secretary   Custodian   Teacher

_____

_____

_____

_____

Read each riddle. Who can help with the problem? Draw a line to that person.

1. I am sick today. Who should my dad call at school?

2. My friend spilled her milk. Who can help clean it up?

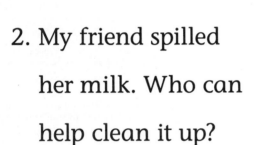

3. My mom wants to know about school rules. Who should she ask?

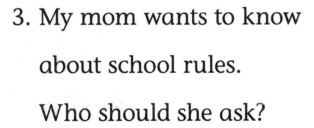

4. I want to learn about animals. Who can help me?

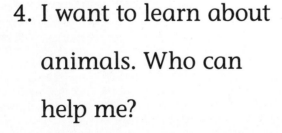

Look at the chart. Do you know these leaders?

Leader	Symbol	Role	One thing this leader does
Mayor		Head of a city	Looks after city streets and parks
Governor		Head of a state	Gets help for people in floods
President		Head of a country	Helps make laws for the United States

Listen to each riddle on the next page.

Use the chart above to find the answer.

1. When there are floods, I get help for the people

   in my state.

   I am the _____.

2. I am the leader of the United States.

   I am the _____.

3. If your city streets need fixing, you can talk to me.

   I am the _____.

Look at your handout.

1. Who is the helper on your page? Circle one.

   Teacher　　　Principal　　　Secretary　　　Custodian

2. Think about a person who does this job in your school. What is this person's name?

   _____

3. Draw some ideas for your page.

What is one way you help others at home?

Write or draw what you do.

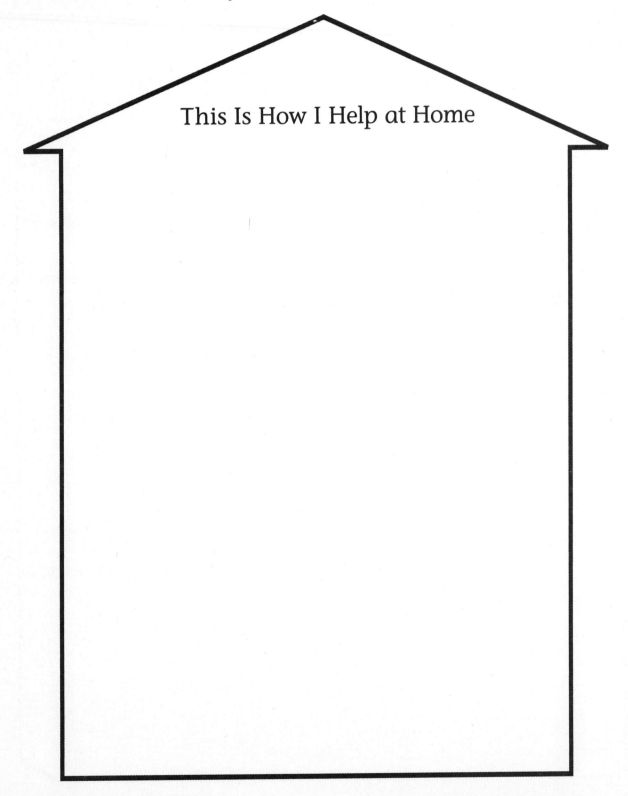

This Is How I Help at Home

List two ways you are nice to others at school.

1. _____

2. _____

Draw one way you are nice to others at school.

● List two ways you take care of your things at school.

1. _____

2. _____

Draw one way you take care of your things at school.

_____

List two ways you do your best at school.

1. _____

2. _____

Draw one way you do your best at school.

List two ways you respect others at school.

1. _____

2. _____

Draw one way you respect others at school.

Part A

Clara Barton lived long ago. She lived by the Golden Rule. List three things that Clara did to help people.

1. _____

2. _____

3. _____

Part B

Look at the pictures of Clara Barton in the Reading Further. What is one way that life in the past was different? Draw or write your answer.

Part C

If Clara were alive today, in what ways might her life be the same?

Hint: Think about the ways that she helped people.

Draw a picture of yourself working with Clara. What are you both doing? Who are you helping?

Think about the Helping Hand
Award you will make.

Who is a good helper at your school?

_____

How is that person a good helper?

_____

See the person in your mind. What is your helper
doing? Who is being helped? Draw some ideas. Use
your drawings on your award.

Have you ever seen maps like these?

What do you think they show? Write your ideas.

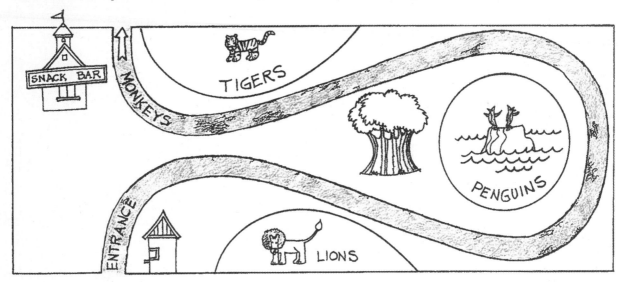

This map shows _____.

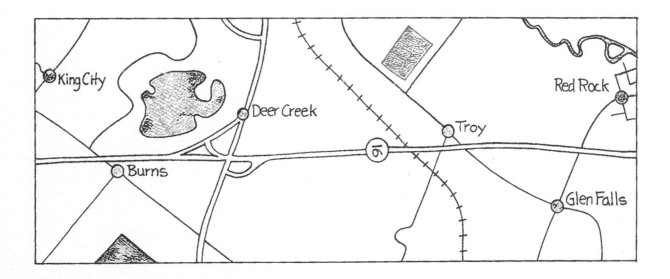

This map shows _____.

Color the map. Follow these steps:

1. Draw a brown line around the classroom.

2. Color the door orange.

3. Color the round tables green.

4. Color the cabinet orange.

5. Color the teacher's desk brown.

6. Color the student desks blue.

7. Color the wastebasket yellow.

8. Color the computer black.

9. Color the rectangular table red.

10. Color the symbols in the map key to match your map.

Map of Ms. Hutchinson's Classroom

Map Key

Door	/
Round table	○
Cabinet	▭
Teacher's desk	▯
Student desk	▢
Wastebasket	○
Rectangular table	▯
Computer	🖥

N E S W (compass rose)

Look at the maps that follow.

Choose the map you would use for each

need. Write the kind of map in the blank.

1. I want to find what is north of my state.

   I need a _____ map.

2. I want to find the school nurse's office.

   I need a _____ map.

3. I want to find City Hall.

   I need a _____ map.

4. I want to find Africa, where elephants live.

   I need a _____ map.

School Map

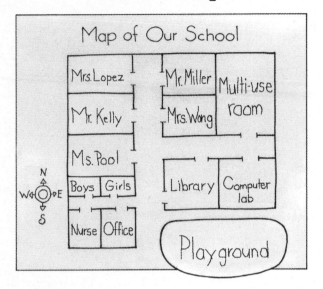

Town Map

United States Map

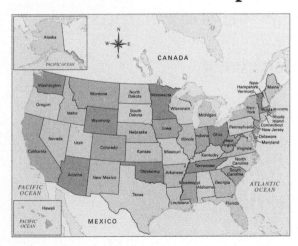

World Map

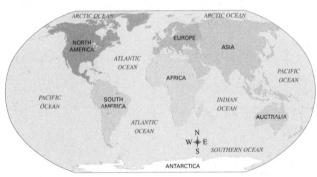

Make a new classroom map. Use the symbols on your handout.

1. Color each symbol.

2. Cut out each symbol.

3. Glue the symbols on the map.
   Make this classroom look different!

4. Color the map key to match your map.

5. Write the letters N, S, E, and W on the compass rose to point north, south, east, and west.

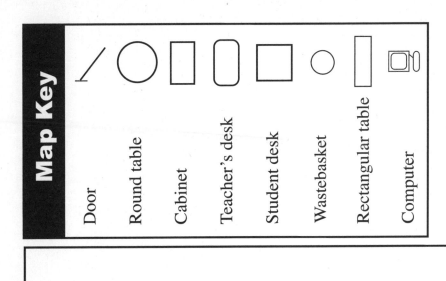

Map Key

Door	/
Round table	○
Cabinet	□
Teacher's desk	▢
Student desk	□
Wastebasket	○
Rectangular table	▯
Computer	

Classroom Map

The past is all the time before today.

The past is last week. It is last year.

The past is when your parents
were young. It is when your
grandparents were young.

JANUARY

SUN	MON	TUE	WED	THUR	FRI	SAT
			1	2	3	4
5	6	7	8	9	10	11
12	13	14	15	16	17	18
19	20	21	22	23	24	25
26	27	28	29	30	31	

What does the past make you
think of? Draw a picture.

On the left, draw two objects you would find in a school long ago. On the right, draw two objects you would find in a school now.

Schools Long Ago	Schools Now
1	1
2	2

On the left, draw two objects students used in school long ago. On the right, draw two objects students use in school now.

Student Life Long Ago	Student Life Now
1	1
2	2

This is a timeline. It shows Mister Bob's long life.
Add what he saw in his lifetime. Cut pictures from
your handout. Glue them in order.

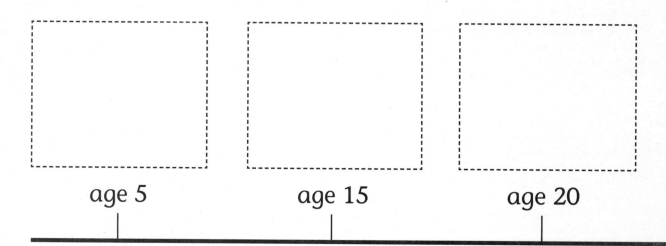

age 5   age 15   age 20

Make a timeline of your
life. Guess what you will
be doing in the future.

Draw a picture for each
time. Write your age.

My Past

age _____

age 30

age 60

age 99

My Present

My Future

age _____

age _____

Things change over time. You read about schools of the past. Now think about schools of the future. Draw something that future schools might have.

How will this be used in future schools?

_____

_____

1. List something that you do with others.

_____

Draw a picture of what you do.

```
┌─────────────────────────────────────────────┐
│                                             │
│                                             │
│                                             │
│                                             │
│                                             │
│                                             │
│                                             │
│                                             │
└─────────────────────────────────────────────┘
```

2. List something else that you do with others.

_____

Draw a picture of what you do.

```
┌─────────────────────────────────────────────┐
│                                             │
│                                             │
│                                             │
│                                             │
│                                             │
│                                             │
│                                             │
└─────────────────────────────────────────────┘
```

Choose a word. Write it next to its picture.

Then write a sentence about that group.

school	family	community

_____

_____

_____

_____

_____

_____

Tell one thing you have learned from your family.

Write what you learned and who taught you.

Then draw a picture to go with your sentence.

I learned _____

from my _____ .

Draw a school group that you belong to.

Write what you are doing in the picture.

_____

_____

Draw a family group that you belong to.

Write what you are doing in the picture.

_____

_____

Draw a community group that you belong to.

Write what you are doing in the picture.

_____

_____

What does family mean to you? Fill in the word web. Write one word in each box.

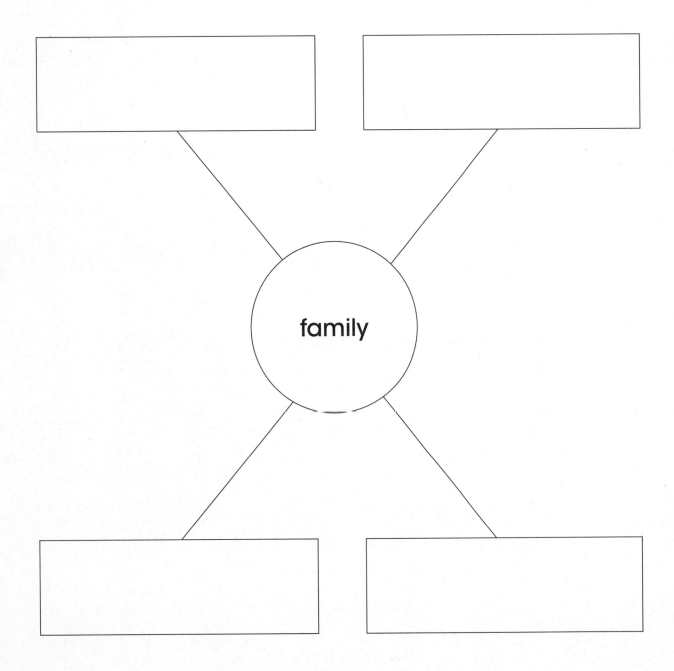

Name four different family members.

_____

_____

_____

_____

● Name three kinds of homes.

Name three family activities.

_____

_____

_____

Draw a picture postcard of your community.

Then write about the place where you live.

_____

_____

_____

_____

Why is your family special?

Finish the sentence. Draw a picture.

My family is special because _____

_____ .

Draw four things that families buy.

Write the name of each one.

Circle whether each picture shows a need or a want.

need   want

need   want

need   want

need   want

need   want

need   want

● List three jobs that are connected to writing and selling a book.

_____

_____

_____

Draw a picture of a special job in your community.

●

Complete each sentence.

What _____ did you pay for the mini-book?

Our class is a type of _____.

Your group made a _____ about which good to buy.

The mini-book is a _____. It is something we would like to have.

The apple is a _____. It is something we have to be healthy.

Word Bank				
choice	need	market	price	want

Popcorn has a long trip from the field to the bowl. Draw or write at least four steps along the way. Number your steps in order.

In the end, a boy got something he wanted—popcorn. What did all the workers get?

_____

Draw and label one need and one want.

Complete the sentences.

This is a need because

_____.

This is a want because

_____.

Write one word to answer each question.

Draw a picture.

1. What does your family need
   to grow and stay healthy?

   _____

2. What does your family need
   to keep warm outdoors?

   _____

3. What does your family need
   to protect them from wind
   and rain?

   _____

Complete the sentence. Draw a picture.

In my family, we help each other by

_____.

Complete the sentence. Draw a picture.

In my family, we share what we know by

_____.

Complete the sentence. Draw a picture.

In my family, we show feelings by

_____.

● Complete the sentence. Draw a picture.

In my family, we spend time together by

_____.

Plan a poster about taking care of Earth.

What is your pledge? _____

_____

Think about the scroll you will make.

Draw or write some ideas for your scroll.

1. How can you help your family with chores?

2. How can you share what you know with your family?

3. How can you show that you care about your family?

4. How can you bond with your family?

Draw a picture of you as a baby.

Draw a picture of you now.

Have you changed?   yes   no

Think about your family over the past few years.

What is one thing that has changed?

_____

_____

Draw a picture to show that change.

Think about how life will change when you are older.

1. Draw a chore you will do when you are older.

2. Draw something new you will do when you are older.

Write two sentences about how Ted's family has changed.

1. _____

_____

_____

2. _____

_____

_____

Think about what each object was used for.

Next to each picture, draw what we use today.

Draw a picture of your family now.

Draw a picture of your family in the future.

How could you find an answer for the questions below? Match each question to a good source.

What is the weather in Chicago, Illinois?

● ●

What bodies of water are near Washington, D.C.? ● ●

What do people do for fun in Seattle, Washington? ● ●

1. Draw a picture of where you live. Write the name of your town or city.

2. What water and landforms does your family live near? Draw a picture.

Source:

My Question: _____

3. What is the weather like where your family lives? Draw a picture.

┌───┐
│   │
│   │
│   │
│   │
│   │
│ Source: │
└───┘

My Question: _____

4. How does your family get around where you live? Draw a picture.

┌───┐
│   │
│   │
│   │
│   │
│   │
│ Source: │
└───┘

My Question: _____

5. What does your family do for fun where you live? Draw a picture.

Source:

My Question: _____

_____

6. Draw a picture of one way your family takes care of where you live.

Find out about an event that happened in the past.

Interview a family member.

Event: _____

When did it happen? _____

What happened? Use words and pictures.

Draw a picture. Show two ways how where you live affects you.

Draw one picture for each holiday.

Fourth of July

Valentine's Day

Thanksgiving

Draw a picture of Roberto's birthday party.

Write one way Roberto's birthday is different from yours.

Draw a picture of the Chinese Lantern Festival.

Write one thing you learned about this festival.

Match the American symbols.

U.S. flag ● ●

Statue of Liberty ● ●

bald eagle ● ●

Liberty Bell ● ●

Recite the pledge with your class.

Pledge of Allegiance

I pledge allegiance to the Flag

of the United States of America,

and to the Republic for which it stands,

one Nation under God,

indivisible, with liberty and justice for all.

Sing this song with your class.

America

My country, 'tis of thee,

Sweet land of Liberty,

Of thee I sing.

Land where my fathers died,

Land of the pilgrims' pride,

From every mountainside,

Let freedom ring!

● Draw a picture of an American holiday.

How do we celebrate it?

Holiday: _____

Plan your quilt square. Choose a special day:

_____

List or draw some ideas.

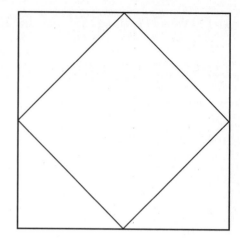

Food	Activities
What do you eat?	What do you do?

Clothes	Decorations
What do you wear?	What makes things pretty?

Draw your home in the center.

Draw four places near your home. Label them.

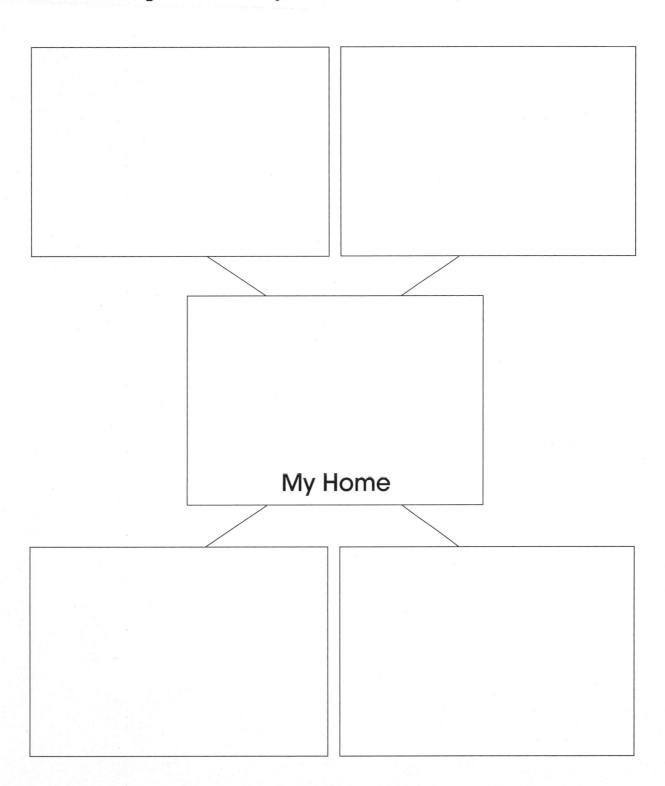

My Home

Circle sentences that describe a good neighbor.

We say hello to our neighbors.

We keep our yard clean.

We walk our dog on a leash.

We pick up trash in
our neighborhood.

We pick our neighbors' flowers
without permission.

We let our dog run in our
neighbor's yard.

We wave to our neighbors.

We water our neighbors' plants
when they go away.

We feed our neighbors' pets
when they go away.

We drop trash on the street.

What Do Good Neighbors Do? **99**

Good neighbors help each other. Read these two problems. How could a neighbor help?

Choose one problem. Write your ideas for helping out.

_____

_____

Give yourself an award.

Draw yourself being a good neighbor.

Write what you did.

Cover and Title Page:
Getty Images

Lesson 1

4T: Enigma/Alamy
4TC: iStockphoto
4BLC: Thinkstock
4BRC: Dmitriy Shironosov/Dreamstime
4B: Thinkstock

Lesson 4

26T: Hongqi Zhang (aka Michael Zhang)/
Dreamstime
26TC: iStockphoto
26BC: iStockphoto
26B: iStockphoto

Lesson 10

66TL: Thinkstock
66TR: Thinkstock
66CL: Thinkstock
66CR: Thinkstock
66BL: Thinkstock
66BR: Thinkstock

Lesson 12

83T: Culver Pictures Inc./SuperStock
83C: Brian Hagiwara/RF/Brand X/Corbis
83B: iStockphoto

Lesson 13

85T: Thinkstock
85C: Thinkstock
85B: Lajo_/ Dreamstime

Lesson 14

93T: Lawrence Weslowski Jr /Dreamstime
93TC: Nicholas Burningham/Dreamstime
93BC: Sean Pavone/Dreamstime
93B: Filtv/Dreamstime
94: Vasili Cazacu/Dreamstime